Usborne
Travel
Activity
Pad

Written by Phil Clarke and Simon Tudhope

Designed by Michael Hill and Marc Maynard

Edited by Sam Taplin

Additional designs by
Ruth Russell and Nayera Everall

Tunnel traffic

Which line will be the fastest through the tunnel, and which will be slowest? Add up the boxes that each vehicle is carrying. The smaller the total, the quicker the traffic.

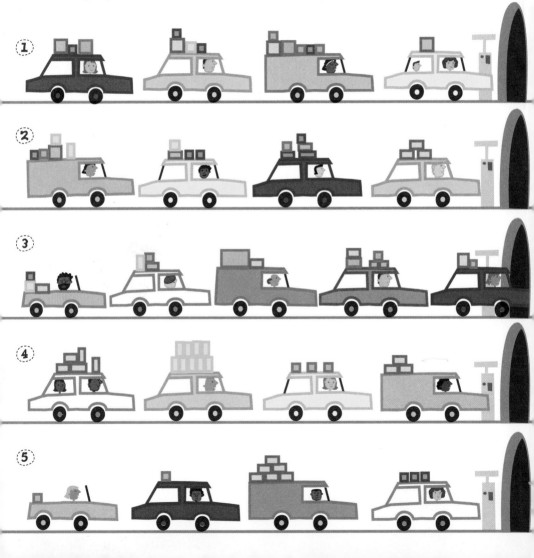

Crazy carousel

Guide the luggage to the people waiting below.

Safari adventure

Draw what you can see from your jeep.

Triangle tiles

Reach the end while stepping only on red, yellow and green triangles. You can move through sides, but not corners.

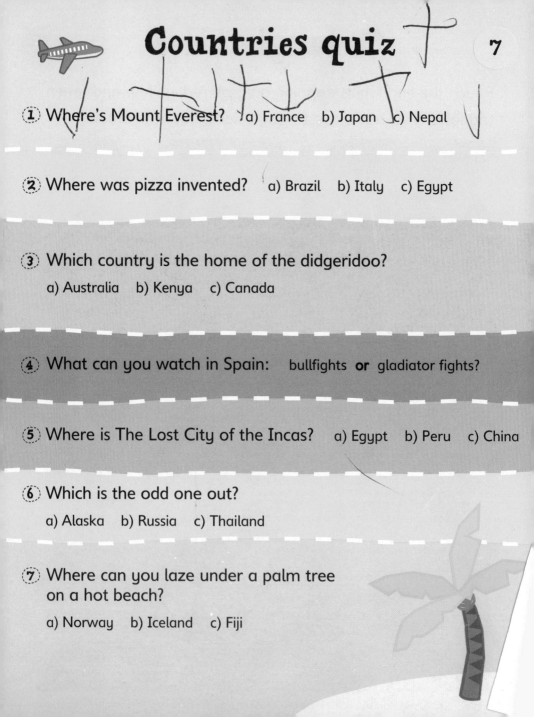

Countries quiz

1. Where's Mount Everest?   a) France   b) Japan   c) Nepal

2. Where was pizza invented?   a) Brazil   b) Italy   c) Egypt

3. Which country is the home of the didgeridoo?
   a) Australia   b) Kenya   c) Canada

4. What can you watch in Spain: bullfights **or** gladiator fights?

5. Where is The Lost City of the Incas?   a) Egypt   b) Peru   c) China

6. Which is the odd one out?
   a) Alaska   b) Russia   c) Thailand

7. Where can you laze under a palm tree
   on a hot beach?
   a) Norway   b) Iceland   c) Fiji

Flag challenge

Trace over all the dotted lines of the two flags below, without taking your pencil off the paper or going along any of your lines twice.

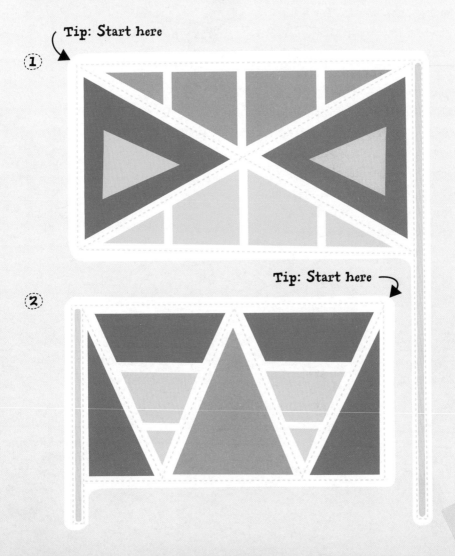

Tip: Start here

1

Tip: Start here

2

Treasure hunt

Follow the directions below to find the buried treasure.

Sail east till you can sail no more, then south. At a land good to live upon, head west, then south at a place unfit for life. Sail east to save your own life, then south to the smoking mountain. Head west to an island. Turning south, hug its coast till you see the bay of death to your southwest. Now sail west as far as you can, and dig for treasure between two trees.

Rocks

Start here

Dead Beach

Village

Skull Island

Shark Cove

Whirlpool of Doom

Fire Island

N
W   E
S

Bug box

Fill the grid with these four bugs. Each row, column and four-square block must contain one of each.

Canoe camp

Help Gemma paddle back
to the campsite.

Flying home

Guide the pilot from airport to airport, back home.
Avoid the red airports, because they have no fuel.

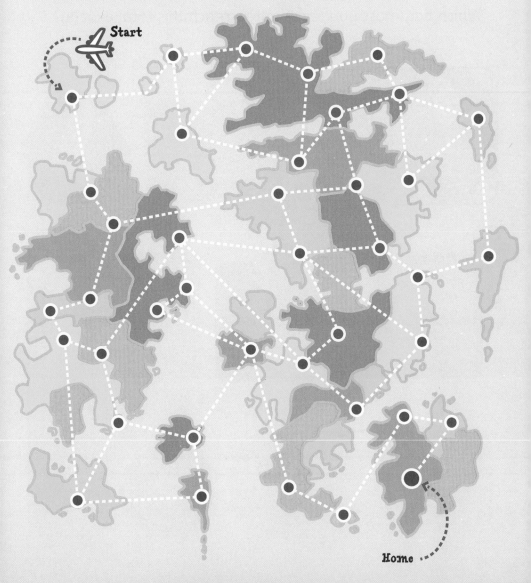

Start

Home

Excess baggage

Your travel party is going on a small plane, but has too many bags for the flight. You can take 200kg altogether. Which bag must you leave out to reach this total exactly?

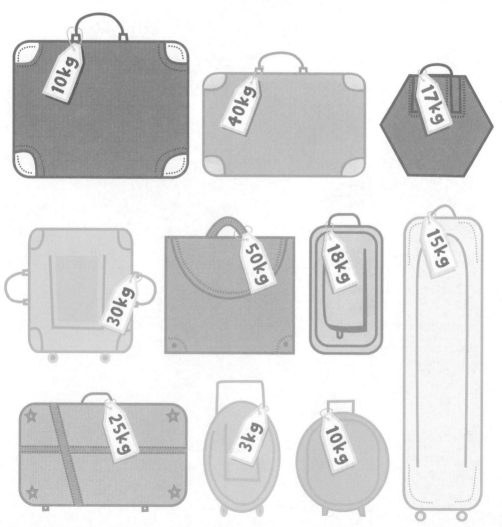

10kg

40kg

17kg

30kg

50kg

18kg

15kg

25kg

3kg

10kg

Taj Mahal

Draw in the other half of this famous Indian monument.

Make a clown face

Follow the instructions on page 190 to fold this page into a clown's face.

Cut or tear along this dotted line

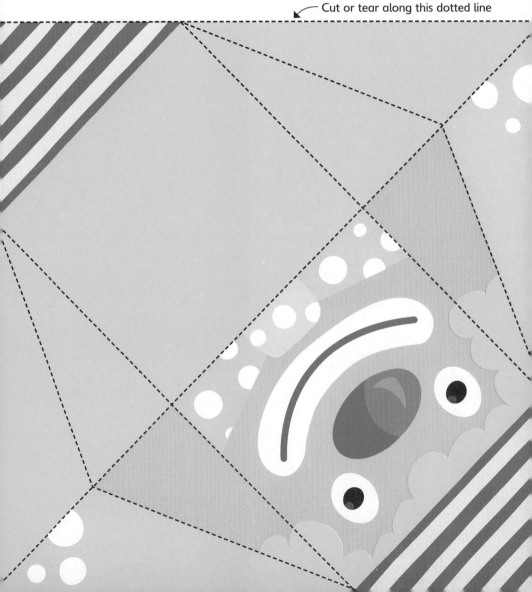

Send a postcard

Write a postcard to a friend, then design some stamps to send it on its way.

Car games

1 Place chain

Name a place. Then the next player says a place whose
name starts with the last letter of your place, and so on.
For example, France... Edinburgh... Hawaii...

2 Now!

One player picks something in the distance, such as a
bridge. They say what it is, then close their eyes. When
they think the car has reached it, they call out 'Now!'

3 20 Questions

One player thinks of a famous person or character. The
next player tries to guess who it is by asking up to 20
questions that can only be answered yes or no.

Campers beware...

Which are there more of in this campsite:
bears or campfires?

Talking hippo

A hippo at London Zoo has learned to talk. He's interviewed by the zoo's paper. Fill in the gaps to complete the article.

You can trust...

ZOO NEWS

A Hungry Hippo

Last night at London Zoo, Horace the hippo looked at his dinner, let out a big sigh and said "Not lettuce again!" Now, in an exclusive interview, he talks about his life at the zoo.

Reporter: Hello, Horace. How are you?

Horace: I'm fine thank you, John.

Reporter: How did you learn to talk?

Horace: ....

....

....

....

Pictured: A disgruntled Horace

Reporter: Do you like living at the zoo?

Horace: ....

....

....

Reporter: And finally, what would you like to eat for dinner, instead of lettuce?

Horace: ....

Cityscape

Use your pens to complete this city scene.

Seashore search

There are all kinds of things on this beach, from sunglasses to sea creatures. But can you find something out of place?

Airport race

Add up the answers for each trail to find the plane with the biggest total. That plane will reach the airport first.

12+4

20-19

11-9

1+2

12x3

8-3

4+6

8x2

14-9

7x3

15+5

9-4

6x2

7-3

Draw a sandcastle

Follow the steps to draw your own sandcastle.

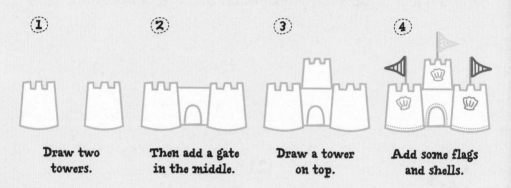

1 Draw two towers.

2 Then add a gate in the middle.

3 Draw a tower on top.

4 Add some flags and shells.

Treasure maze

Navigate your way to the treasure, but don't dare to pass beneath the sea monsters' giant tentacles.

Magic square

In a magic square, the numbers in every row, column and diagonal add up to the same total. Write the missing numbers from one to nine in the empty boxes so that the numbers in every row, column and diagonal add up to 15.

Silly jokes

1 How can you tell if an elephant has been in your refrigerator?

2 What can fly underwater?

3 Girl: "Daddy, there's a man with a beard at the door."

4 What do you call a boomerang that doesn't come back?

5 What do you call an alien with no ears?

6 Why are goldfish orange?

7 What's big and red and eats rocks?

8 Where does a half-ton gorilla sit at the movies?

Answers

1. Footprints in the margarine

2. A parrot in a submarine

3. Father: "Tell him I've got one already."

4. A stick

5. Anything you like: he can't hear you!

6. Because the water turns them rusty.

7. A big, red rock-eater

8. Anywhere it wants!

Optical illusion

Do the little squares spiral into the middle, or are they in separate circles? Turn to the Answers at the back to find out for sure.

Across the sea

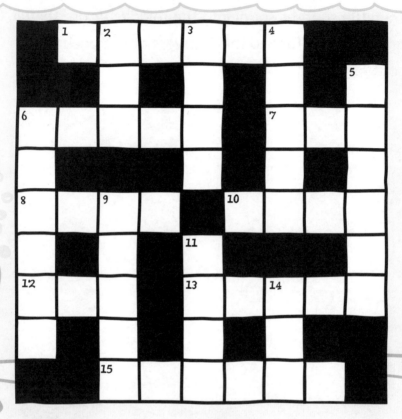

Across

1. Weight that holds a ship in place (6)
6. Room on a ship (5)
7. Spider's home (3)
8. On top of (4)
10. Thought or plan (4)
12. Use your eyes (3)
13. Strange (5)
15. Six, for example (6)

Down

2. Tip of a pen (3)
3. Unclenched fist (4)
4. Moved a boat, using oars (5)
5. On a ship (6)
6. Sea voyage for pleasure (6)
9. Huge area of saltwater (5)
11. Move through water using arms and legs (4)
14. Frozen water (3)

Quick-draw speedboat

Draw a line that races to the island as fast as you can, keeping within the pale blue route. Time yourself to test your speed.

FINISH

Adding apples

Add apples to the empty trees in the orchard so that the apples in each row add up to 17. Each tree must have between one and nine apples, and no two trees can have the same amount.

Find the fish

Find the one fish on this page that isn't part of a pair, and draw around it.

Chatty penguin

See the instructions on page 188 to fold this page into a talking penguin.

Explorers quiz

① **Which fierce warriors discovered Iceland, Greenland and North America?** a) Romans   b) Mongols   c) Vikings

② **In which direction does a compass needle point?**
a) East   b) West   c) North

③ The explorer who discovered Australia was called Captain...
a) Butcher   b) Baker   c) Cook

④ Who explores time and space in a blue police box?
a) Sherlock Holmes   b) Doctor Who   c) Darth Vader

⑤ Who discovered the land of the Oompa-Loompas?
a) Willy Wonka   b) Captain Nemo   c) Harry Potter

⑥ Where might you find the lost city of Atlantis?
The bottom of the ocean **or** buried in the desert?

⑦ Who sailed to America in the 15th century?
Neil Armstrong **or** Christopher Columbus?

Tower maze

Help the brave knight climb up the vines to reach the dragon. He can start from the bottom of any vine.

Finish

How to draw a car

Add some cars to the roads by following these steps:

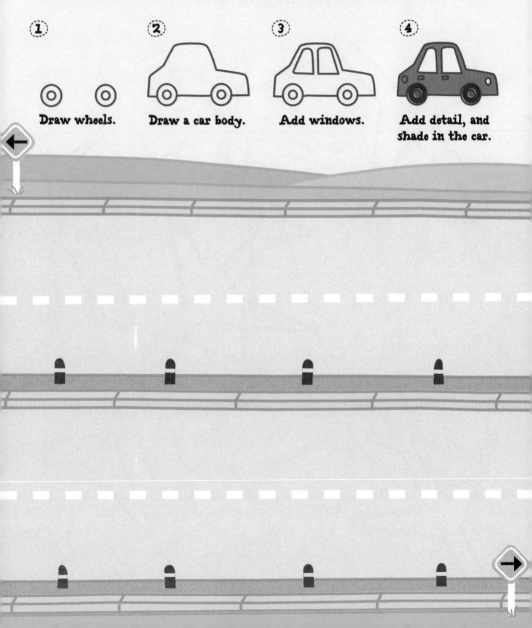

① Draw wheels.

② Draw a car body.

③ Add windows.

④ Add detail, and shade in the car.

Air traffic

How many planes can you count here?

Spy climb

Help the spy climb up to the roof without being seen. He can't cross a lighted window and he can't move diagonally.

Hot-air balloons

Give these balloons a lift by adding bright patterns.

Sail the seas quiz

1 What sank the *Titanic*?

a) a huge wave   b) a torpedo   c) an iceberg

2 Which vessel travels underwater?

submarine **or** pedalo?

3 What did Vikings sail in?

dinghies **or** longships?

4 Who was a famous pirate?

a) Whitebeard   b) Blackbeard   c) Yellowbeard

5 What did sailors use to sleep in: hammocks **or** haddocks?

6 Which country can't be reached by boat?

a) Spain   b) Switzerland   c) France

7 What did pirates call the bottom of the ocean?

a) Davy Jones' locker   b) Mother Hubbard's cupboard

c) Billy Bones' chest

The Game of Y

In this game, each player takes turns to fill a hexagon with their own mark. The first to make a patch of hexagons that touches all three sides of the triangle is the winner. Black won the game below. The other triangles are blank for you to play.

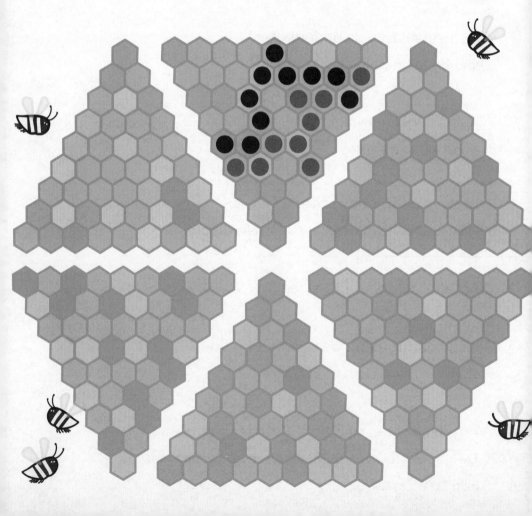

Fortune teller

Turn to page 187 for instructions on how to fold this page
into a fortune teller, then ask it where you will travel this year.

Cut or tear along this dotted line

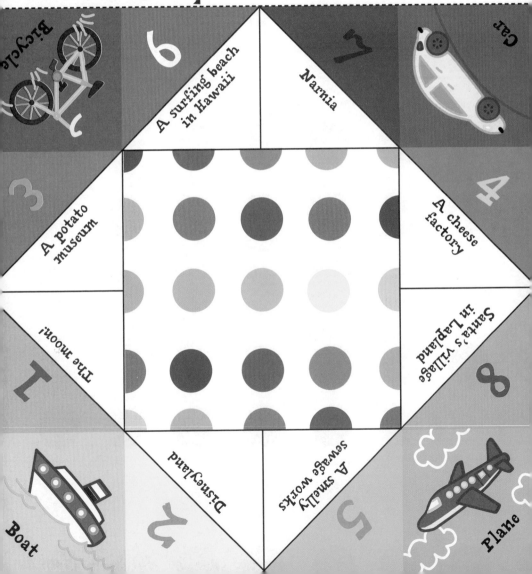

Pier puzzle

Find your way along the piers from the big ship that's just arrived.

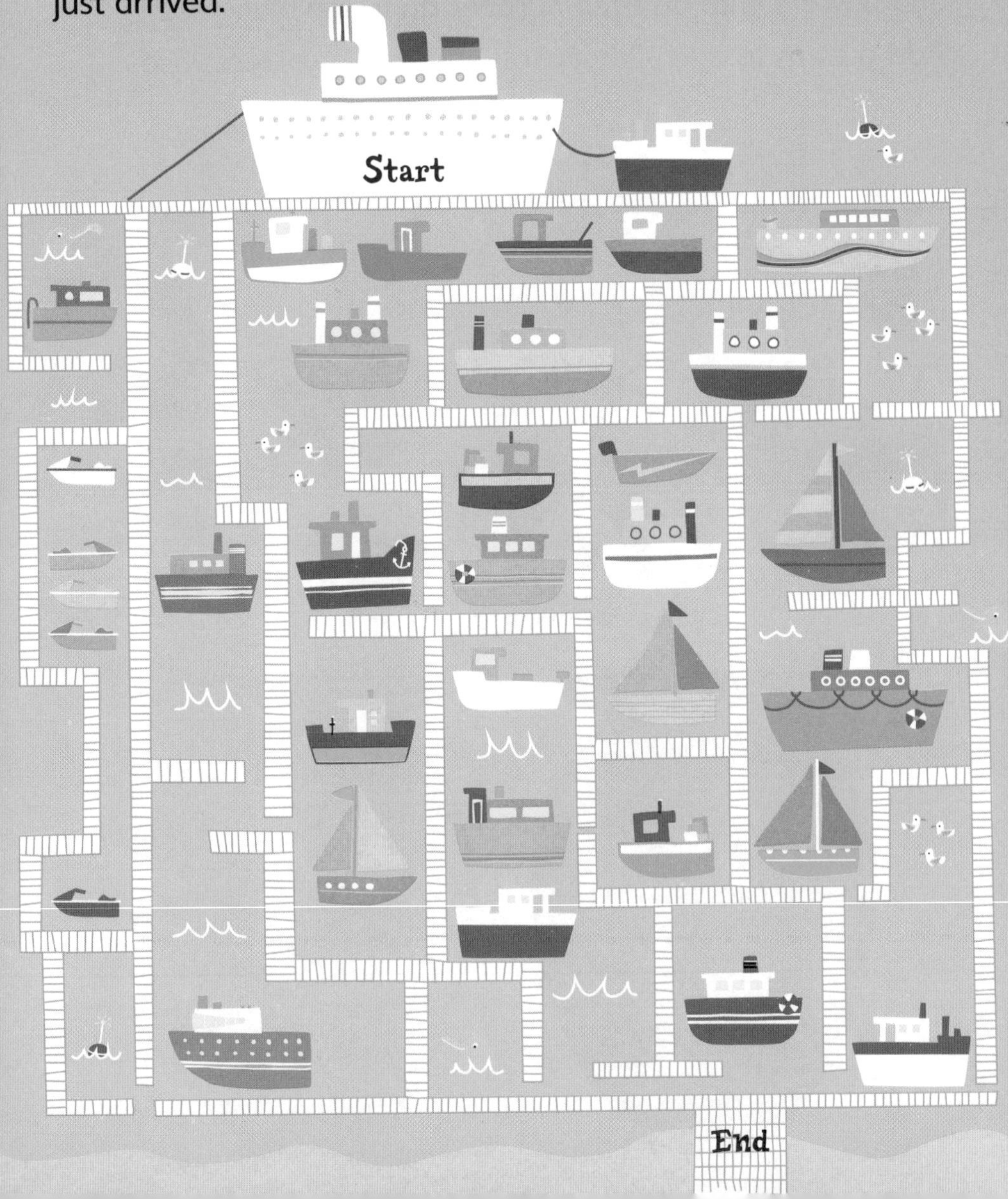

Start

End

Sorting stems

Flowers with an odd number of petals go in the red vase
and flowers with an even number go in the blue vase.
Add a stem to each flower to put it in the correct vase.

Tongue twisters

Say each tongue twister as fast as you can.

1. Peter Piper picked a peck of pickled peppers.
   If Peter Piper picked a peck of pickled peppers,
   where's the peck of pickled peppers
   Peter Piper picked?

2. If Stu chews shoes, should Stu choose the shoes he chews?

3. How much wood would a woodchuck chuck
   if a woodchuck could chuck wood?

4. I scream, you scream, we all scream for ice cream!

5. She sells seashells on the seashore.
   If she sells seashells on the seashore,
   she'll be sure to sell seashore shells.

6. The big black bug bit the big black bear, but
   the big black bear bit the big black bug back!

Hidden picture

Shade the spaces with a blue dot blue, those with a green dot green, and so on. What does the picture show?

Bees or spiders?

Turn each circle into either a bee or a spider so that there are twice as many bees as there are spiders.

Spider

Bee

Fairground maze

Guide the cars along the tracks of the
fairground ride to reach the exit.

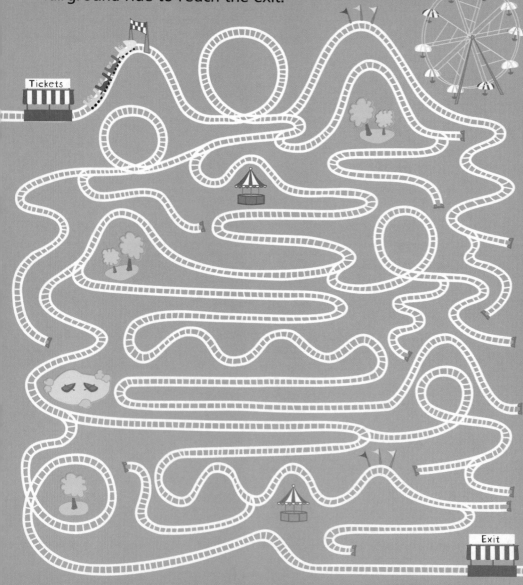

Word cross

Put a letter in the middle of each X
to make four different three-letter
words in each one.

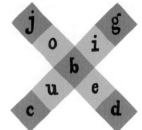

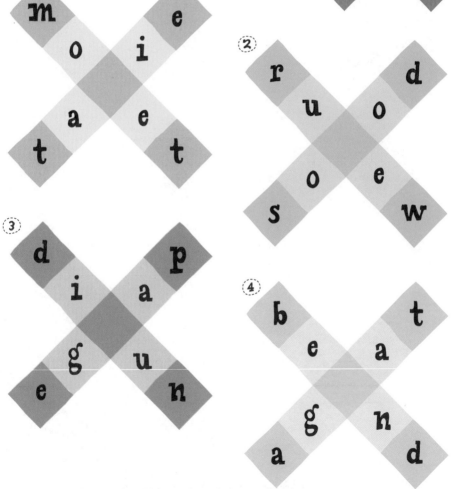

Spaghetti junction

The car that drives under the most bridges will reach the railway bridge first. Which will it be?

49

Divide the world

See how this plane's flight path has cut the Earth into two parts. Try to split the Earth into seven parts by adding just two more straight lines.

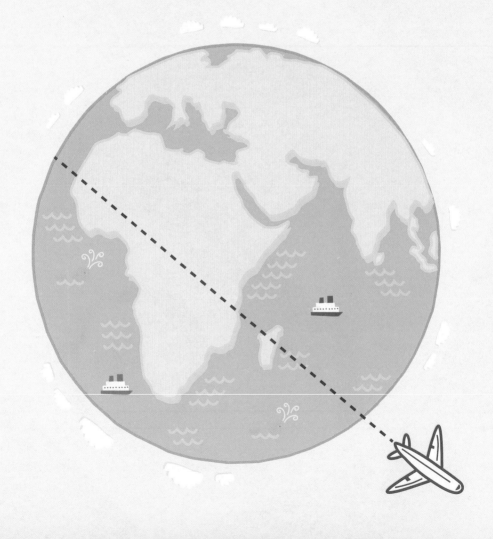

Space rocket

Follow the instructions on page 190 to fold this page into a model rocket.

Cut or tear along this dotted line

On your bookshelf

Give funny titles to all these books.

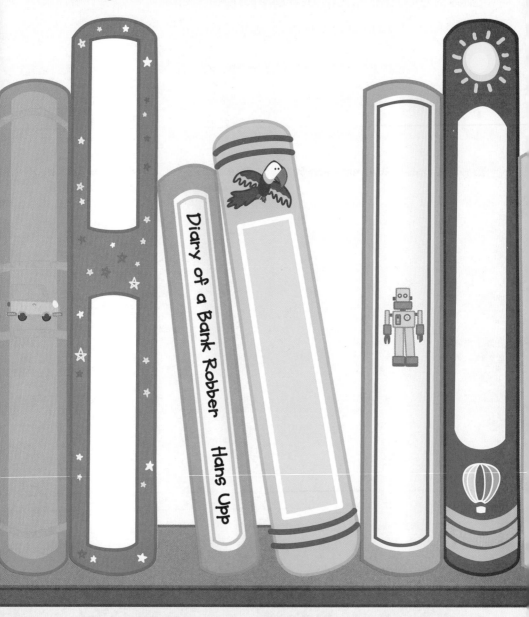

Diary of a Bank Robber

Hans Upp

Draw a butterfly

Create a butterfly by following these steps:

① Draw a body.

② Add some wings.

③ Give it two feelers.

④ Add the details, and shade it in.

Packing penguins

All these penguins are ready for a break, but just one line matches the black silhouette. Which one?

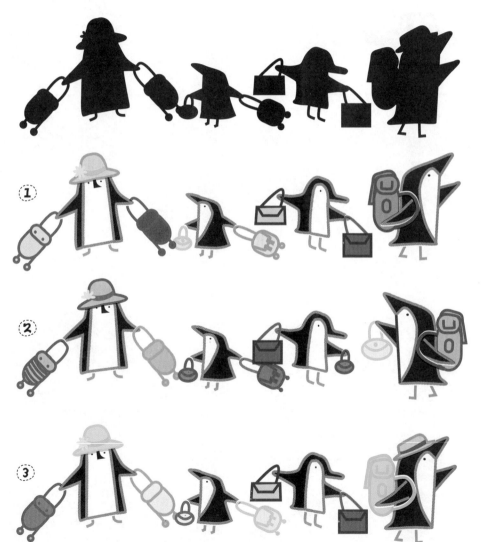

Quick-draw highway

Draw a line that races along this road, as fast as you can, but don't go off the sides.

FINISH

Eyes peeled

You can play this game alone or with friends. Everyone gets a card and sees how quickly they can spot all the things on it.

Cut or tear along the dotted lines

Card 1 ✓

Dog

Red car

Train

Picnic table

Boat

Card 2 ✓

Burger bar

Speed limit sign

Blue car

Fire truck

Bird

Card 3 ✓

Plane

Motorcycle

Hotel

Police officer

Pizza place

Card 4 ✓

Church

Ambulance

Truck

Stop light

Baseball cap

Card 5 ✓

Bus ☆

T-shirt ☆

School ☆

Yellow car ☆

River ☆

Card 6 ✓

Horse ☆

Supermarket ☆

Backpack ☆

Glasses ☆

Baby ★

Card 7 ✓

House ☆

Balloon ☆

Cow ☆

Billboard ☆

Traffic cone ☆

Card 8 ✓

Bicycle ☆

Farm ☆

Mailbox ☆

Cat ☆

Bridge ☆

Fact or fiction?

1. The Ancient Greeks invented boomerangs.

2. There are still dinosaurs in Japan.

3. People have swum from England to France.

4. Your heart skips a beat when you sneeze.

5. You can see the Pyramids of Giza from space.

6. Chocolate is poisonous to dogs.

7. Michael Jackson was the first person to walk on the Moon.

8. The capital of the USA is New York.

9. David Beckham is a famous boxer.

10. A chimpanzee was flown into space.

Crossword

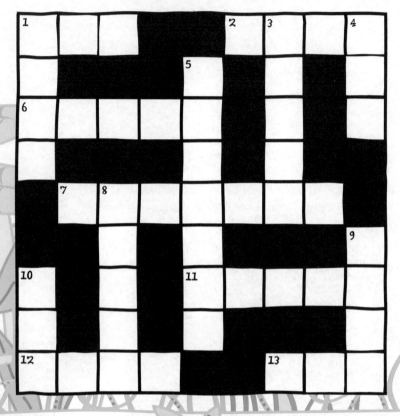

Across

1. 1+2+3 (3)
2. Happy (4)
6. Bilbo's adopted son (5)
7. Dracula, for example (7)
11. Picture (5)
12. Story (4)
13. Type of tree (3)

Down

1. Couch (4)
3. "Sooner or _____" (5)
4. Noise, racket (3)
5. Smart, whale-like sea animal with long snout (7)
8. Fourth month (5)
9. Look for (4)
10. Hole (3)

Dot-to-dot

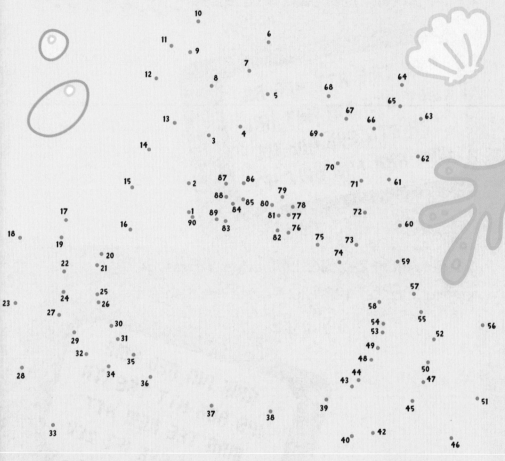

Connect the dots to bring this sea creature to life.

Code breaker

Special Agent X has left a secret message using
a code he calls 123. Can you crack it?

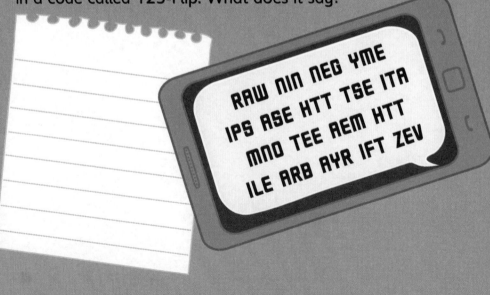

A dangerous journey

Help Red Riding Hood find her way to Granny's house, avoiding all the wild animals and blocked paths.

Happy fish

Give the fish scales, and doodle more fish in the white spaces.

Seashore jumble

You might see all these things at a beach. How many can you count jumbled up below?

Staring owl

Follow the instructions on page 189 to fold this page into an owl.

Cut or tear along this dotted line

The dragon's hoard

You are a knight seeking the lair of a dragon who has stolen the king's gold. Look at the key to find out what to do at certain map symbols:

Key

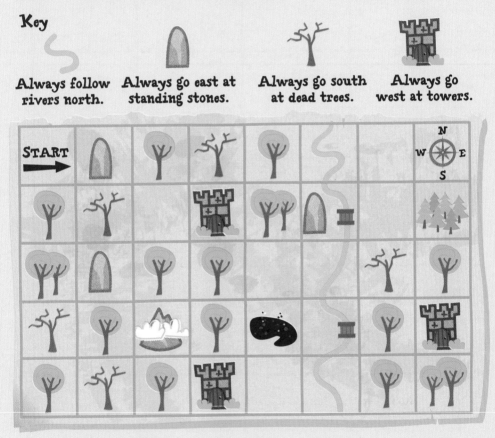

Always follow rivers north. Always go east at standing stones. Always go south at dead trees. Always go west at towers.

Is the dragon's lair:

In Fog Mountain?

In the Black Lake?

In the Wild Woods?

Optical illusion

The dark red lines across this grid are slanting: true or false? See the Answers at the back to find out.

Animal quiz

1. Which legendary half-man, half-ape creature is said to live in the Himalayas: Bigfoot **or** the Abominable Snowman?

2. Which of these animals live near the North Pole:
   polar bears **or** penguins?

3. In India, what type of snake do snake charmers use?
   a) python   b) cobra   c) mamba

4. A group of lions is known as a:
   a) pride   b) greed   c) sloth

5. Blue whales are the biggest animal that's ever lived.
   True **or** false?

6. What do camels store in their humps?
   water **or** fat?

7. What does a vampire bat drink:
   blood **or** water?

8. Which of these is a badger's home?
   a) lodge   b) sett   c) warren

Star-crossed

Cross out all the types of shapes listed at the bottom of the page, then write out the letters of the remaining shapes to find a place full of stars.

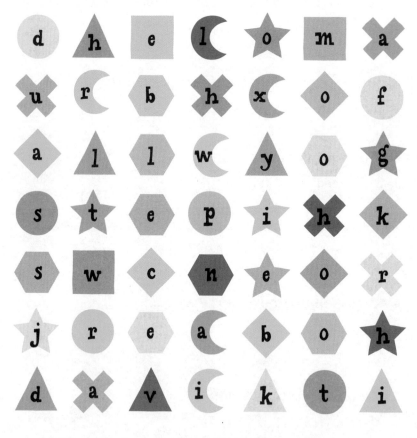

Yellow shapes   Circles   Pink shapes   Stars   Xs

Moons   Red shapes   Green shapes

....

How to draw birds

Follow these steps to draw some dainty garden birds.

1 Draw two bodies
with legs.

2 Add a beak to
each body.

3 Give the birds
feathery tails.

4 Now add wings
and shading.

Find the bag

Your bag, luckily, is slightly different from the rest.
Which one is it? Write your initials on the label.

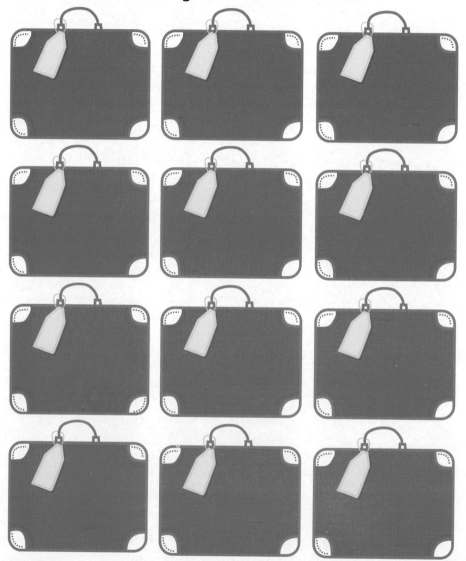

Hours of fun!

1. **Don't say 'Yes'** In this game, everyone asks one player questions, such as, 'Are you awake?' They must reply truthfully, without saying 'Yes'. For example, 'I must be, because I'm talking to you!'

2. **Oh no! But...** Create a story that switches from bad to good, then back to bad, and so on. For example:

   Laura: Oh no! A hungry bear is coming our way!
   Michelle: But he only wants some honey.
   Vicky: Oh no! My hands are covered in honey!

3. **Hand writing** Close your eyes and hold out your hand. The other player thinks of a word and traces each letter on your palm. You've got to guess the word.

4. **Would you rather?** Take turns posing tricky choices to each other. For example, would you rather be able to fly or turn invisible? Have two noses or three eyes? Be poor but popular, or rich and hated? Be unable to laugh or unable to lie?

Camping break

Fill this scene with as many tents as you can.

Desert maze

Find your way to the oasis, avoiding the snakes, vultures and sinking sand.

Start

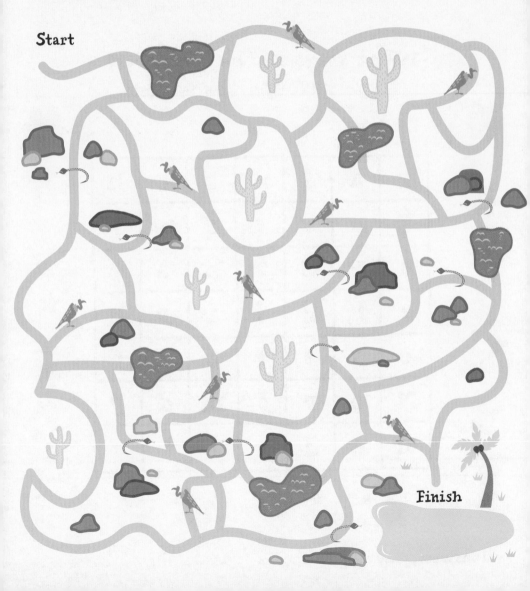

Finish

Riddle grid

Cross out each letter of the riddle below, in the grid, then rearrange the remaining letters to see its answer.

What stays in the corner yet travels around the world?

r	a	s	w	a	t	h
t	o	v	e	s	w	t
e	y	s	t	h	a	t
a	h	n	l	i	r	n
c	s	e	t	o	a	r
y	o	r	e	m	d	p
u	n	d	r	l	t	e

Answer:..

Optical illusion

Hold this page about 30cm (12 inches) away and stare at the black dot for 30 seconds. What happens to the blobs? Check the Answers at the back.

Follow the instructions on page 189 to fold this page into a monster.

Cut or tear along this dotted line

Giraffe's supper

This giraffe eats 10 leaves every 30 minutes. How many hours of eating are left on this acacia tree?

Food cube

This layout can be folded to make only one of the boxes below. Which one?

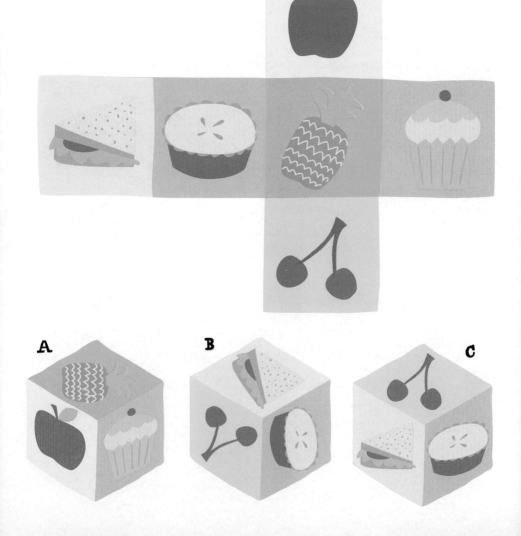

A

B

C

Truth or lie?

1. Astronauts have landed on Mars.

2. When it's summer in Britain it's winter in Australia.

8. Lions live in the Amazon rainforest.

3. More people speak Chinese than any other language.

7. The Sun moves around the Earth.

4. Greenland is covered in trees.

6. Only twelve people have ever walked on the Moon.

5. 70% of the Earth's surface is covered by land.

At the park

It's a fine day to be at the park. Draw more people playing sports, flying kites, or whatever else you can think of.

Draw a rabbit

Make a rabbit by following these steps:

① Draw a body and head.

② Add some legs.

③ Give it ears and a tail.

④ Add a face, and shade it in.

Baggage stack

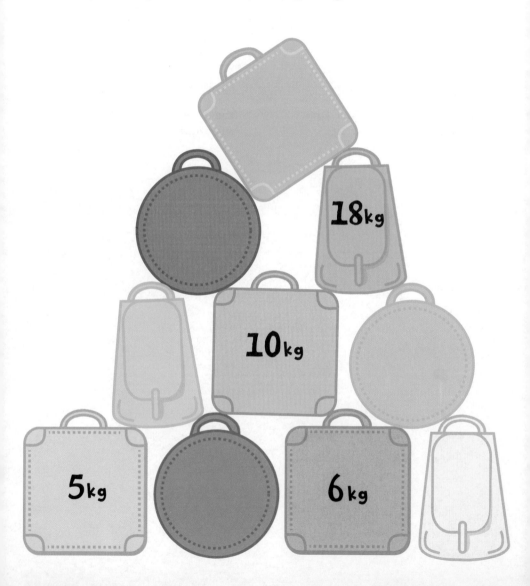

The weight of each bag is the sum of the two bags it's resting on. Try to fill in the missing weights.

18kg

10kg

5kg

6kg

Mountain lodge

Guide these hikers through the trees to the lodge, where they can warm up with a hot drink.

A Strange Discovery

One day at school you knock on the teacher's door. No one answers. You're about to leave when you notice a blue light glowing inside. The door creaks open. What's that in the corner? It's a time machine! There's no one around, so you step inside and turn the dial.

Write what happens next...

....

....

....

....

....

....

....

Jungle grid

Look for these pieces in the jungle picture below.

 = f1   =   =   =   =

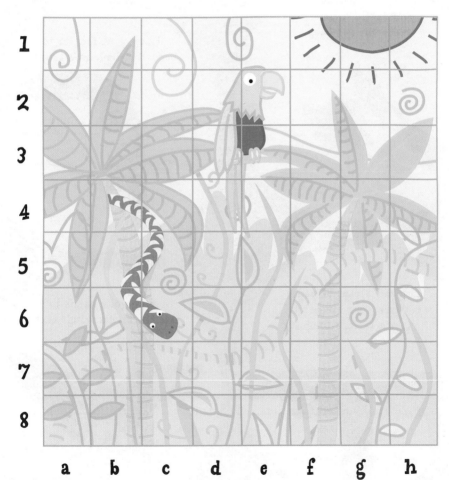

Made of shadows

Wait till it's dark and shine a light on the wall.
Then try making these shadow animals.

Open and close
your little fingers to
make the dog bark.

Flick your fingers to
bend the elephant's trunk.

Put two strips of paper
between your fingers to
make a snake's tongue.

Flap your hands to
see the bird's wings beat.

Draw a lion

Bring the King of the Beasts to life by following these steps:

1 Draw a head and a mane.

2 Add front legs and paws.

3 Give it two back legs and a tail.

4 Add details and shade it in.

What do you see?

What do you see in these doodles? Make up your mind then look upside-down for some of our ideas.

A pig in a bush

A person looking down a hole

A person looking through a keyhole

A spider doing the splits

A dead snowman

Pea soup

A tomato on a diving board

A worm doing a headstand

A truck in the mud

Weather symbols

Find the value of the symbols and fill in the missing one.
The sum of each line and column is shown.

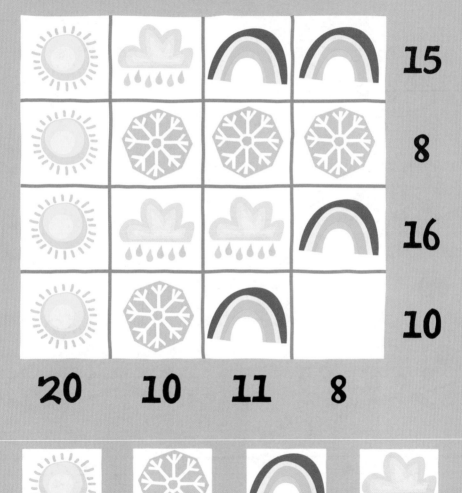

Flying saucers

One of the flying saucers in this alien fleet is different from the rest. Which is it?

Chase the ball

Draw a line from the boy to the ball as quickly as you can. But don't wander onto the grass!

Optical illusion

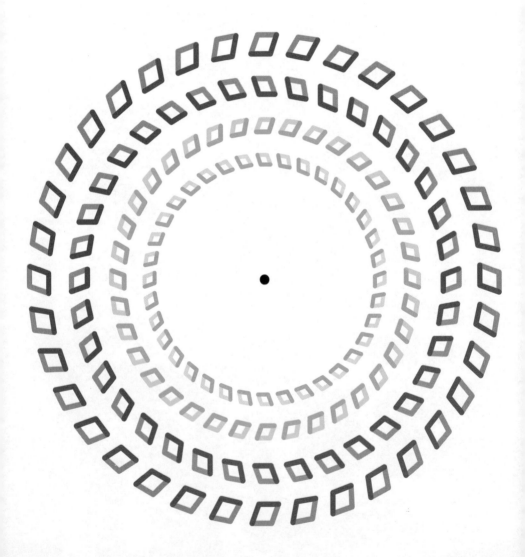

Move your face closer to the black dot, then away again.
Do the circles seem to turn? Check the Answers at the back.

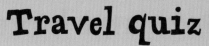

Travel quiz

1 What's the opposite of southwest?

2 Which Italian city is known for its many canals?

a) Venice   b) Rome   c) Florence

3 Which ocean is so deep it could cover Mount Everest?

a) Indian   b) Atlantic   c) Pacific

4 Where might you see the Loch Ness monster?

a) Germany   b) Scotland   c) Morocco

5 Which is NOT a real place?

a) Transylvania   b) Lapland   c) Gotham City

6 In London, where can you see waxworks of famous people?

The Houses of Parliament **or** Madame Tussauds?

7 Where is the Bermuda Triangle said to be?

The Sahara Desert **or** the Atlantic Ocean?

Dots and boxes

This two-player game can be played with pens and paper, or even on a beach with pebbles and sand.

Make a square grid of dots as big as you like, then take turns joining two dots with a line. Every time you finish a box, you write your initial inside and get another go. When no more lines can be added, the player with the most boxes wins.

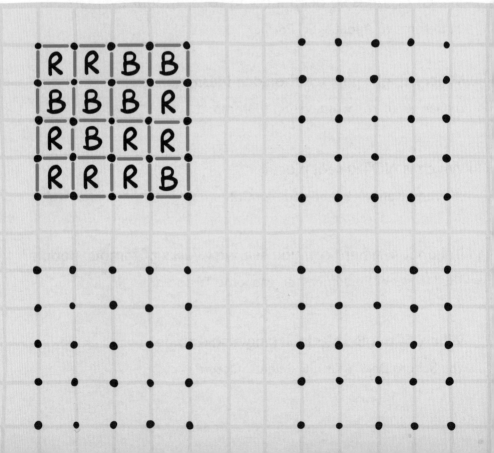

Capital cities

Find the six countries and their capital cities, listed at the bottom, in the grid. They can be written in any direction.

J	C	H	I	N	A	G	N	N	E	G
K	R	G	N	D	G	L	A	W	A	V
T	E	A	A	W	E	I	W	O	P	A
A	M	N	I	N	R	N	A	T	N	U
L	A	R	Y	O	M	O	T	E	A	S
C	G	O	B	A	A	Y	T	G	I	T
B	E	I	J	I	N	G	O	R	G	R
T	T	A	N	A	Y	U	G	O	R	A
I	O	B	E	N	I	L	R	E	B	L
D	G	N	A	W	T	O	N	G	O	I
T	A	R	R	E	B	N	A	C	H	A

Beijing	Berlin	China	Canada
Guyana	Nairobi	Kenya	Australia
Germany	Ottawa	Canberra	Georgetown

Draw lines to match each city to the correct country.

Design souvenir keyrings from all over the world.

Dare snapper

97

Turn to page 187 for instructions on how to fold this page into a dare snapper, then let it pick dares for you and your friends.

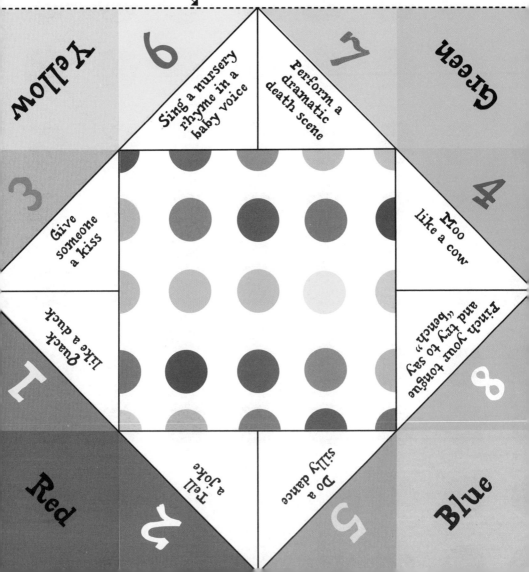

Cut or tear along this dotted line →

Yellow

6

Sing a nursery rhyme in a baby voice

1

Perform a dramatic death scene

Green

3

Give someone a kiss

4

Moo like a cow

1

Quack like a duck

Pinch your tongue and try to say "bench"

8

Red

2

Tell a joke

Do a silly dance

5

Blue

Car number fun

Games with vehicle plates for one or more players:

1 Use the letters in a plate to make up the silliest phrase you can. For example, BST could stand for "Baboons Smell Terrible".

AD51 BST   76-MH   DAE·057·WLP

2 Make up stories from the letters. The first letter starts the name of your main character. The second is for what that character is doing. The third is for the thing he's doing it to. So **SRW** could start a story where **S**uperman **r**escues a stranded **w**hale.

3 -SRW   ·6A①NG·   B8F-Y1

3 Look for a plate where all the numbers and letters are in order. For example:

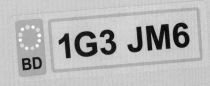
BD 1G3 JM6

Spot the spots

How many bright blue spots are there on this page?

Wild West showdown

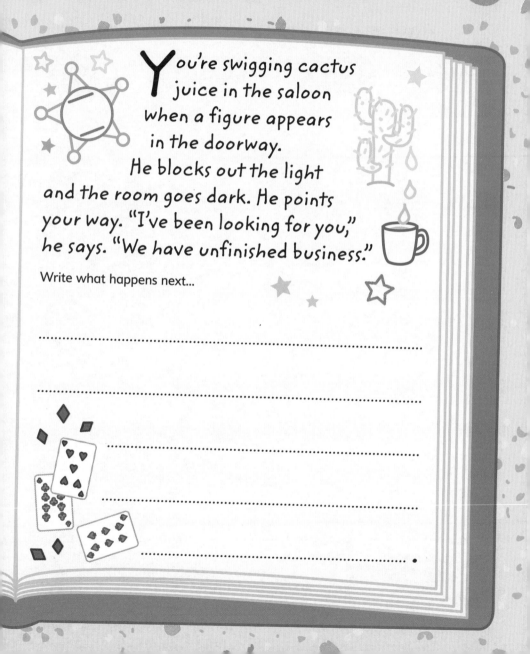

You're swigging cactus juice in the saloon when a figure appears in the doorway.

He blocks out the light and the room goes dark. He points your way. "I've been looking for you," he says. "We have unfinished business."

Write what happens next...

....

....

....

....

....

Airport

Which gate would you pick to get to the plane?

GATE 1   GATE 2   GATE 3   GATE 4

Animal true or false

1. Ostriches bury their heads in the sand.

2. A flea can jump over the Empire State Building.

3. Sharks were around before the dinosaurs.

4. Giraffes clean their own ears with their tongue.

5. Owls are very wise.

6. Elephants are scared of mice.

7. A blue whale's heart is the size of a small car.

8. Flamingos stand on one leg.

9. Crocodiles eat more people than any other animal.

10. Lemmings jump over cliffs.

Optical illusion

103

The circles in the middle row are darker than the others: true or false? See the Answers at the back to find out.

Draw what you think the pilot can see from his window.

Clever flowers

Add the correct number of leaves to the right-hand side of each stem, so that:

Leaves on the left   **x**   Leaves on the right   **=**   Number on the flower

Time zones

The time in London is three hours before the time in Moscow. Mumbai is two and a half hours after Istanbul. Paris is one hour after London. Write the city names under the right clocks.

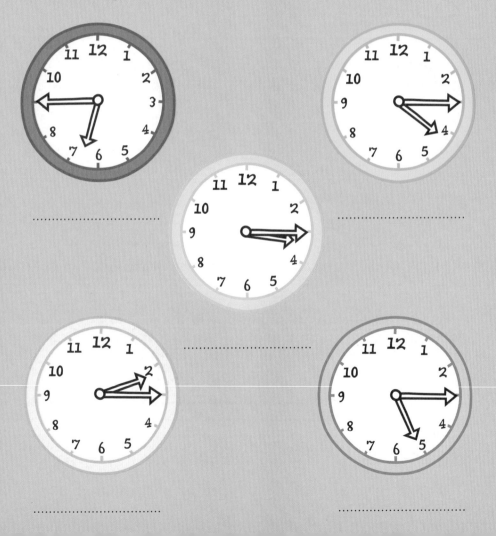

Dot-to-dot

Join the dots to find out what is swimming towards you.

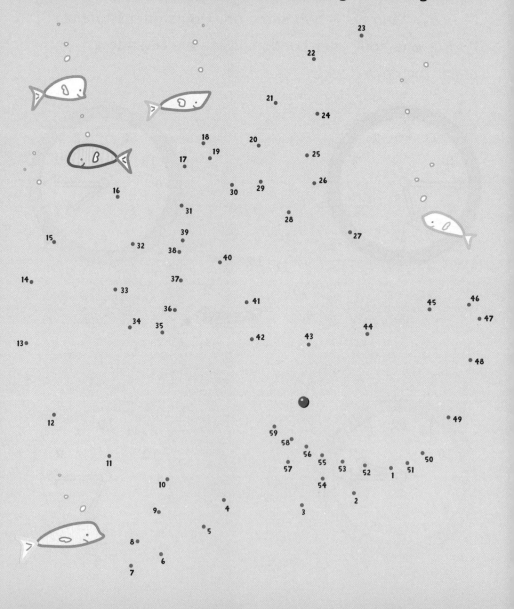

Mummy museum

Draw a line as fast as you can to escape the creepy museum. Take more than a minute, or touch the walls, and the mummies will get you!

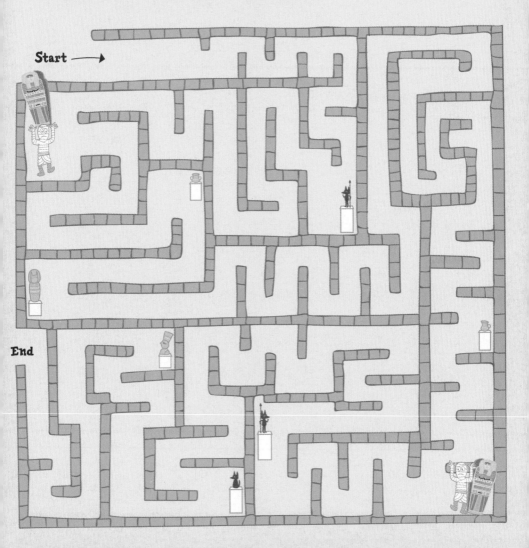

Airport X-ray

Draw what the X-ray machine reveals in your bag.

Riddles

(1) Feed me and I will live, give me drink and I will die.
What am I?

(2) I have a neck, but no head, two arms, but no hands.
What am I?

(3) The more you take away, the bigger I become.
What am I?

(4) I'm tall when I'm young, but short when I'm old.
What am I?

(5) I'm full of holes, yet I hold water very well.
What am I?

(6) Before you can use me, I must be broken.
What am I?

(7) I can be served, but never eaten.
What am I?

(8) I'm lighter than a feather, but no one can hold me for long.
What am I?

Owls on a branch

Follow these steps to
draw some owls along the branch.

1 Draw a head
and body.

2 Give it wings and feet,
and outline the face.

3 Add eyes, a beak,
and more details.

Terrible jokes

1 What do you call a sheep with no legs?

2 What do you do if there's a crocodile in your bed?

3 Who came after the first Roman emperor?

4 What's black and white and goes up and down?

5 What did the skeleton order with his drink?

6 How do you make time travel?

7 What did one snowman say to the other snowman?

8 Why did the cowboy ride his horse to town?

Answers

1 A cloud

2 Sleep somewhere else.

3 The second Roman emperor

4 A penguin on a trampoline

5 A mop

6 Throw a clock in the air.

7 Can you smell carrots?

8 It was too heavy to carry.

Who lives there?

In this game, one person looks for an interesting house. When they see one they ask 'Who lives there?' Everyone takes turns describing who the owners might be.

Big family?

Pets?

Job?

Age?

Dominoes

114

Work out each sequence and add the missing dots.

Doodle clouds

Draw some strange things for the sheep to see in the clouds.

Perching parrots

Only two of these parrots are identical. Which two?

Busy bee maze

Guide the honeybee to the pink flower.

Croaking frog

Follow the instructions on page 188 to fold this page into a frog.

Treasure cave

Fill this scene with enough treasure to make a pirate gasp.

Go-fast fuel

The cars go faster with a high-star fuel. Try to find out which car will go fastest and which will be the slowest.

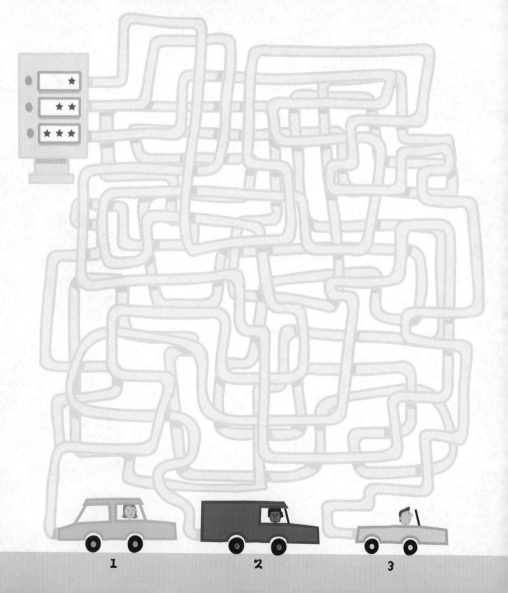

Flags quiz

Unscramble each country name and write its number by its flag.

1) RANCEF..

2) MCAIAJA...

3) PANJA...

4) YGMERAN..

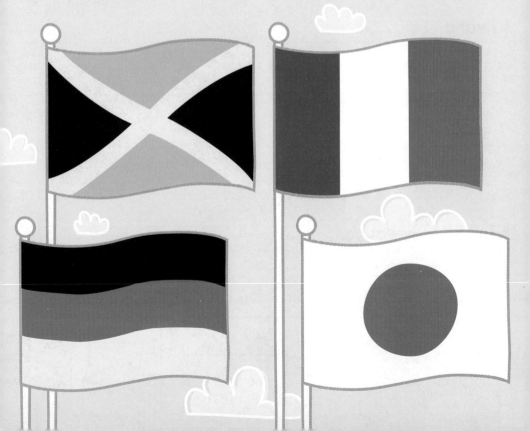

Picture the scene

Close your eyes and picture the best place you've ever been.
Now open your eyes and write about what makes it so special.

When I visited...
....

I saw...
....

....

I heard...
....

....

I smelled...
....

....

I loved it because...
....

....

Spooky house

Add spooky features to this old house.

Up in the air quiz

1 Does it take longer to fly from:

London to New York **or** London to Moscow?

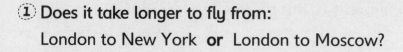

2 Who had a flying carpet?

a) Ali Baba

b) Sinbad

c) Aladdin

3 Modern passenger jets can fly all the way around the world without stopping.

True **or** false?

4 Where does the pilot of a jumbo jet sit?

a) cabin

b) hold

c) cockpit

5 Who flew from England to America in a giant peach carried by seagulls?

a) Charlie

b) James

c) Matilda

Surfboards

Customize these surfboards into wave-riding works of art.

Lots of labels

Your travel party needs 18 luggage labels. Do you need more or less than there are here? How many?

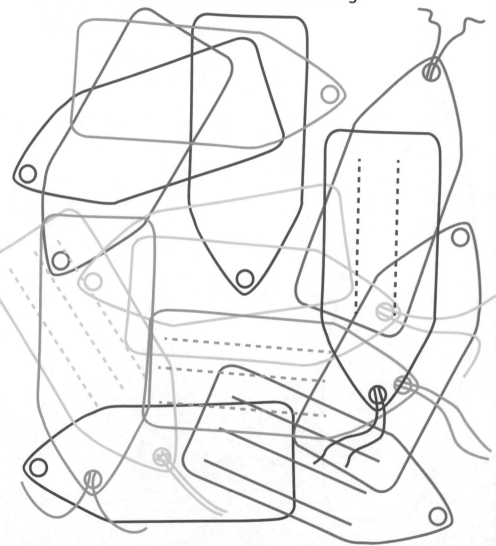

Answer: . . . .

Cluttered campsite

Draw a line from Dan to the beach that touches no tents.

Dan

Doodle zoo

Use your pens to finish the faces of these zoo animals.
Are they happy? Angry? Sleepy? You decide...

Snapping eagle

Follow the instructions on page 187 to fold this page into a snapping eagle.

Cut or tear along this dotted line

Tasty search

Can you find all the foods below hidden in the grid?
They may be written in any direction.

p	s	h	a	r	e	c	l	i	p
c	e	y	e	h	l	h	s	i	f
h	a	a	t	e	p	h	n	m	g
m	p	g	c	u	p	c	a	k	e
j	l	c	e	h	a	d	z	a	w
h	b	u	r	g	e	r	z	s	o
s	a	c	a	l	n	e	i	p	c
z	c	k	e	r	i	z	p	i	e
y	o	b	i	e	p	r	l	h	n
s	n	t	e	s	e	e	h	c	

pineapple   cheese   bacon

chips   pizza   fish

burger   cupcake   peach

Draw planes

Follow these steps to fill the page with planes:

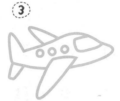

①
Draw a wing.

②
Draw a body, and
the other wing.

③
Add windows
and a tailplane.

④
Add details and
decorate the plane.

Waterhole maze

Help the thirsty elephants find their way along the dotted tracks to the waterhole.

More games

(1) Giggly goose One player thinks of an action word, such as 'swim', but in the game it's replaced by the phrase 'giggly goose'. Everyone asks questions to work out the real word.

Can you giggly goose in the car?

No.

Is giggly goosing fun?

Well, I enjoy it!

(2) Story maker Make a story together. One person starts off with a few words or a sentence, and the others take turns to continue the story.

There was an old woman...

She took it for walks in the park.

...into the duckpond! But the dog had super-powers...

...who had a pet crocodile!

One day, it chased a dog...

Link words

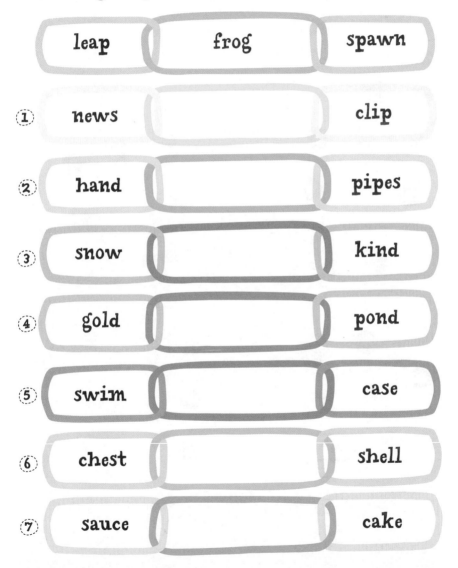

Find a word that can be added to the end of one word
and the beginning of the next. For example:

| leap | frog | spawn |

1. news | | clip

2. hand | | pipes

3. snow | | kind

4. gold | | pond

5. swim | | case

6. chest | | shell

7. sauce | | cake

O or X?

These games will all be finished in one or two turns.

Who will win the most games, O or X?

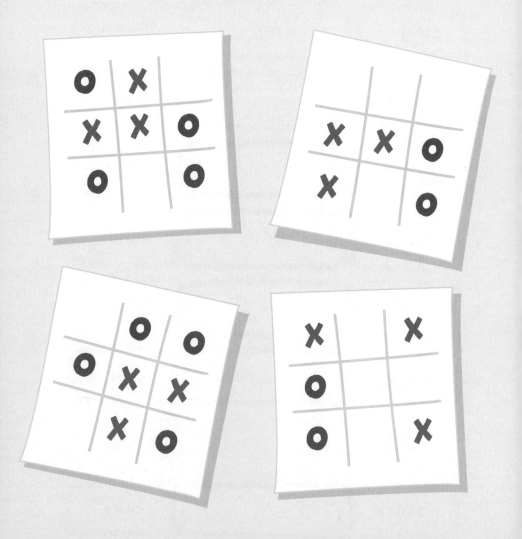

Big Ben

Draw the other half of Big Ben.

Dot-to-dot

What's on the front of this café menu?

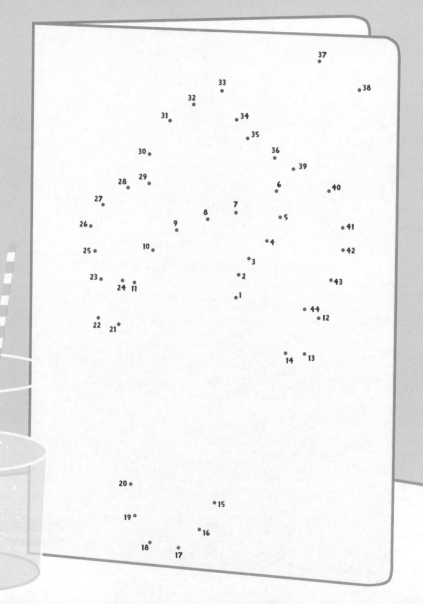

Boomerang mix-up

Who threw which boomerang?

Alien heads

Draw the scariest alien heads you can.

Mini-sudoku

Fill the grid below so that the
numbers 1, 2, 3 and 4 appear
in every line, column, and block of
four squares. Here is an example.

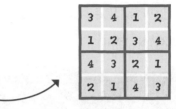

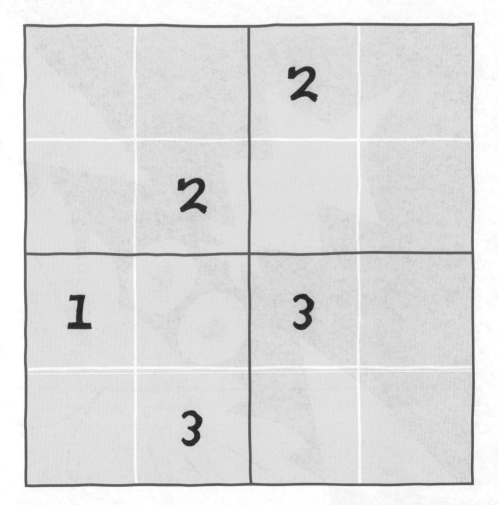

Curious cat

Follow the instructions on page 189 to fold this page into a cat's head.

Cut or tear along this dotted line

Ski run

Guide the skier along the pale blue tracks to the red flag.

Landmarks quiz

1 Which landmark is over 8,000km (5,000 miles) long?

   a) Great Wall of China   b) Grand Canyon   c) Great Barrier Reef

2 Which was NOT one of the seven wonders of the ancient world?

   a) Hanging Gardens of Babylon   b) Pyramids of Giza

   c) Statue of Liberty

3 Where is the Taj Mahal?

   in Africa **or** in Asia?

4 Where were gladiator fights once held?

   a) Colosseum   b) Stonehenge   c) Easter Island

5 Which movie monster climbed New York's Empire State Building?

   a) Godzilla   b) King Kong   c) Count Dracula

6 Which mountain stands beside Cape Town, South Africa?

   a) Table Mountain   b) Chair Mountain

   c) Shelf Mountain

7 Where is the Eiffel Tower?

   a) England   b) Russia   c) France

Slither

This two-player game can be played on a dotted grid of any size, although one side should be longer than the other.

The first player joins two dots, then the next player joins one end to another dot. The loser is the first player that is forced to join the line back up to itself.

Red won this game:

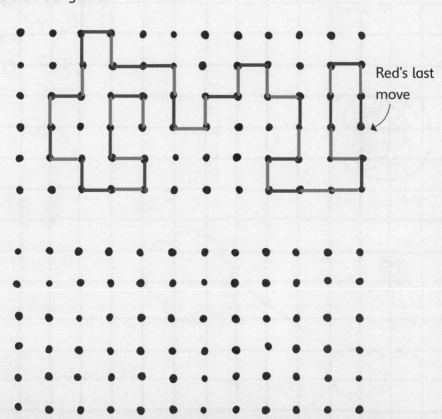

Red's last move

What do you see?

What do these doodles look like to you? Let your
imagination go wild! (Our answers are upside-down.)

A sausage sandwich

Shark-infested
bubble bath

A fat man
walking around
a corner

A monkey
hiding in
a tree

A plate of spaghetti

A spider
waving

A woman doing
the gardening

A woman
walking her dog

People waiting for a bus

Even and odd

Help the mother duck reach her chicks by using only the stepping stones with answers that are even numbers. The father duck must use stones with odd number answers.

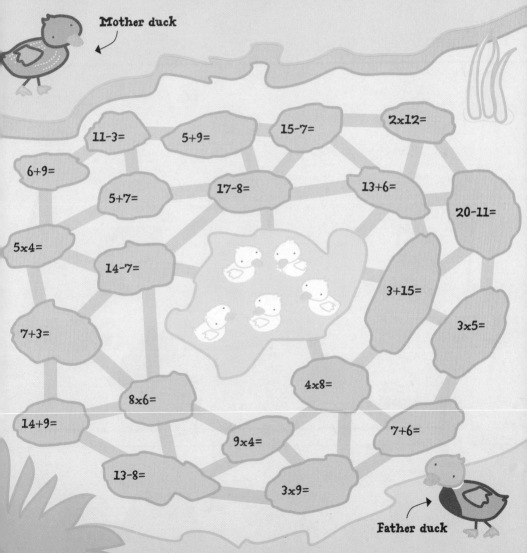

Mother duck

11-3=
5+9=
15-7=
2x12=
6+9=
5+7=
17-8=
13+6=
20-11=
5x4=
14-7=
3+15=
7+3=
3x5=
4x8=
8x6=
14+9=
9x4=
7+6=
13-8=
3x9=

Father duck

Get packing

You need to pack your bag. Try to find and circle all the
things on the list.

Blue shorts
Green shorts
Two t-shirts
Pair of flippers
Snorkel and mask
Sunglasses
Bucket
Swimsuit
Goggles
Sunhat
Sweatshirt
Matching sandals

How to draw kittens  148

Follow these steps to draw some little kittens of your own.

(1) Draw a head and body.

(2) Add a tail and legs.

(3) Then draw a pair of ears.

(4) Now add a face and stripes.

One-way maze

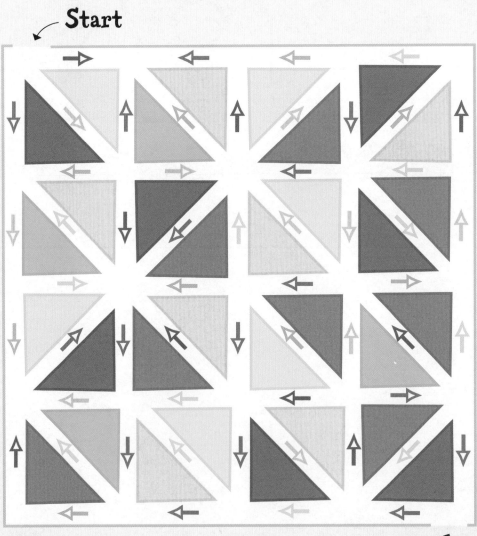

Reach the finish moving only in the direction of the arrows.

Start

Finish

Where in the world?

Write out the letters the ship passes to find out where it's heading.

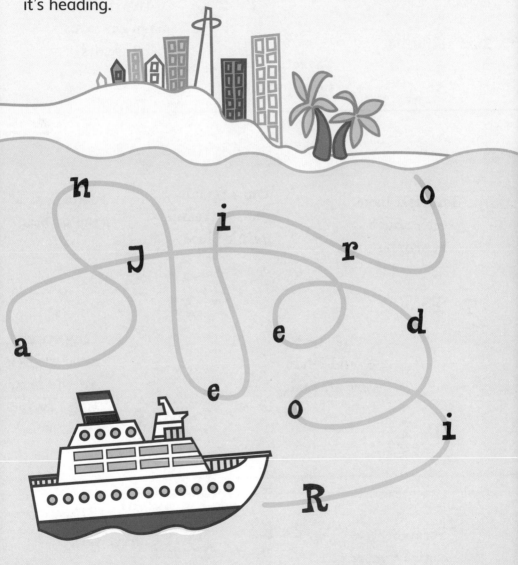

Answer:.................................

True or False?

T F

① Bats are blind.

② Carrots used to be purple.

③ Lipstick often contains fish scales.

T F

T F

T F

④ Goldfish have very short memories.

⑤ Only female mosquitoes drink blood.

⑥ A koala is a kind of bear.

T F

T F

⑦ The first cheerleaders were all male.

⑧ Lightning never strikes in the same place twice.

T F

T F

⑨ Strawberries contain more sugar than lemons.

T F

T F

⑩ Earwigs have wings.

Optical illusion

Can you see ghostly black dots appearing inside the yellow circles? What happens when you try to stare at one? Check the Answers at the back.

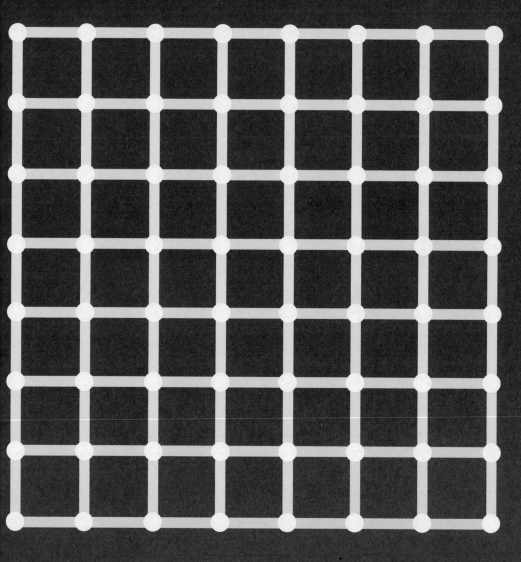

Triangles

Turn each of these triangles into something different.

Weather report

You're a weather presenter: report on the weather so far, then predict tomorrow's weather by circling a symbol.

Yesterday:

Today:

Tomorrow?

Balloon flight

Guide the balloon up between the clouds, avoiding the lightning and rain.

Finish

Famous characters

1. I was a famous outlaw and a deadly archer. I robbed from the rich to feed the poor. **Who am I?**

2. I am the smartest girl in school and superglued my dad's hat to his head. I defeated the evil Miss Trunchbull. **Who am I?**

3. I was a mean old man who was visited by three ghosts on Christmas Eve. **Who am I?**

4. I saw a rabbit with a pocket watch and chased him down a hole. **Who am I?**

5. I work as a plumber and wear a red cap and blue overalls. I rescued Princess Peach from the evil Bowzer. **Who am I?**

6. My boss is M. My colleague is Q. My number is 007. **Who am I?**

7. I have two ugly sisters and lost my glass slipper at the ball. **Who am I?**

Tiger face

Follow the instructions on page 190 to fold this page into a tiger's face.

Cut or tear along this dotted line

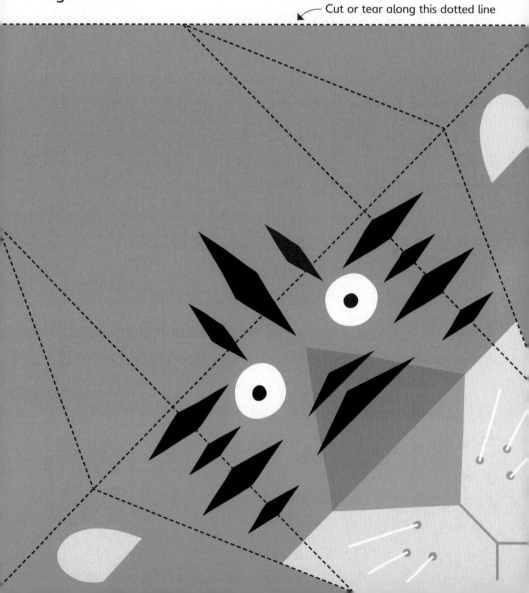

What will be on your in-flight dinner tray? Doodle your ideal meal into the tray compartments.

Diver in danger!

The diver needs to reach the surface, but there are obstacles in the way. Each obstacle has a different number of danger points. Add them up to find the safest route.

Jellyfish
1 point

Squid ink
2 points

Stingray
4 points

Shark
5 points

Picture sudoku

Fill the grid with these four summer treats. Each row, column and four-square block must contain one of each. For example:

Draw a robot

Follow the steps to create your own robot.

①

Draw a body.

②

Give it arms.

③

Add the legs and ears.

④
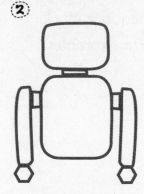

Finish with feet, a face, bolts and shading.

Giggly games

1. Make silly faces but keep completely quiet. See how long it takes for someone to notice.

2. Say the sentence 'You smell like stinky socks' but leave 20 seconds between each word. See if you can get to the end of the sentence without anyone catching on.

3. Take turns asking each other questions. Everyone must answer 'smelly jelly'. The goal is to ask a question that will make the other person laugh when they answer.

What did you have for breakfast?

Smelly jelly!

Honk! Honk!

Make these lanes jam-packed with traffic.

Pyramid maze

You are lost inside a pyramid. Find your way out, while avoiding mummies, skulls and snakes.

START

FINISH

Sunshine Isle

These mixed-up pictures show a flight to the Sunshine Isle.
Put them in the right order.

1 =   2 =   3 =   4 =   5 =

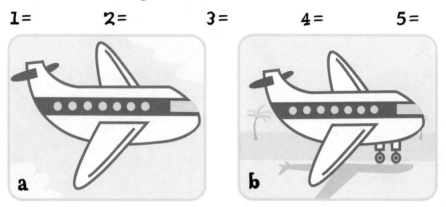

Packing for Paradise

You've won an exotic trip! The country name is hidden in this packing list. Can you find out where you're going?

REMEMBER TO PACK

1 beach towel

5 sunhats

4 snorkels

1 beachball

2 water bottles

1 diving gear

2 or 3 books

1 surfboard

Clue: look carefully at the number next to each item – it may help you!

Answer:......................................

Butterfly hunt

Lily caught the little butterflies, Maddie caught the medium-sized butterflies, and Benji caught the big ones. Count how many each child caught, then shade Lily's yellow, Maddie's red and Benji's blue.

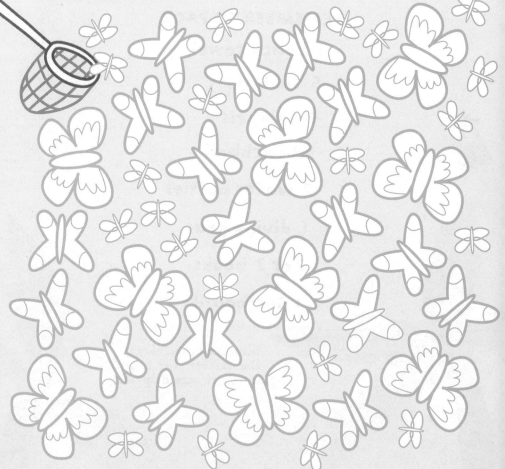

Lily: . . . .   Maddie: . . . .   Benji: . . . .

Crosscram

This two-player game can be played on a dotted grid of any size, although one side should be longer than the other.

The players join pairs of dots, the first joining up and down, the other side to side. Each dot can only be joined to one other. The loser is the first player who can't go.

Blue won this game:

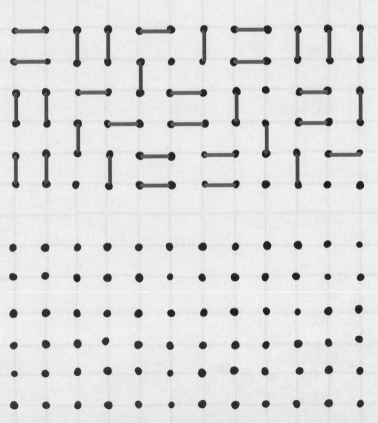

Martian maker

To make a Martian with a friend, tear out this page and fold it along the dotted lines. Secretly draw the Martian's body, then fold it over for your friend to draw the head.

Plenty of penguins

Brrr! Draw more penguins to huddle around
these ones and keep them warm.

Balloon pattern

The shapes on the hot-air balloon follow a pattern –
but some are missing from the bottom white quarter.
Try to draw in the missing shapes.

Fairground game

Come one, come all! To win this game, spot
which prize is not like the others in each row.

Lighthouse

Design the most spectacular lighthouse in the world.

Loopy jokes

1
What do you get if you cross an elephant with a kangaroo?

2
Where was the Queen of England crowned?

3
Where do you find Quebec?

4
What do you call a polar bear in the desert?

5
What has two heads and six legs?

6
Which animal can jump higher than a building?

7
What do you get if you cross a bee with a sheep?

8
What's worse than finding a maggot in your apple?

Answers

(1) **Big holes all over Australia**

(2) On her head

 (3) On a map

(4) **Lost**

(5) A man on a horse

(6) **Most of them — buildings can't jump!**

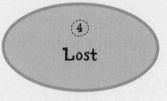

(7) **A striped sweater**

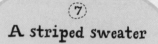

(8) Finding half a maggot

Snapping gecko

Follow the instructions on page 187 to fold this page into a snapping gecko.

Cut or tear along this dotted line

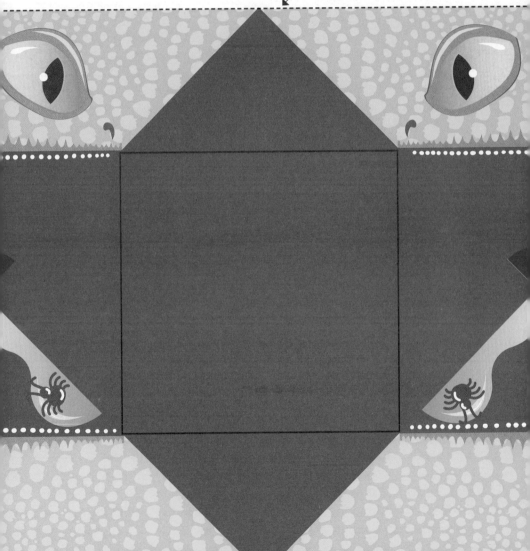

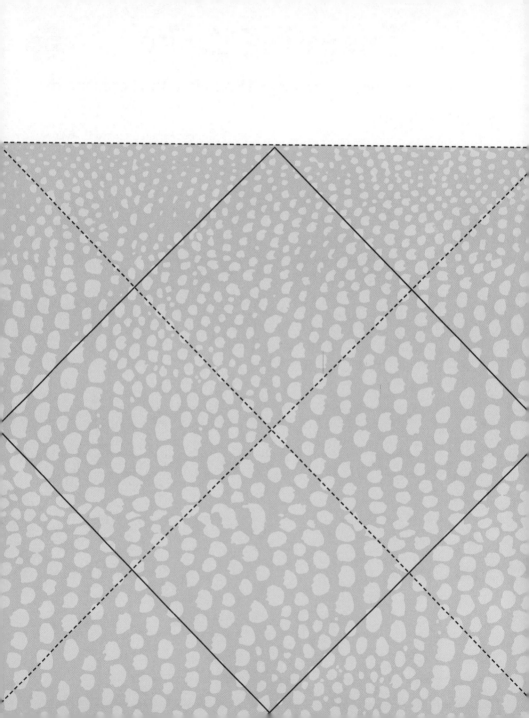

Busy airport

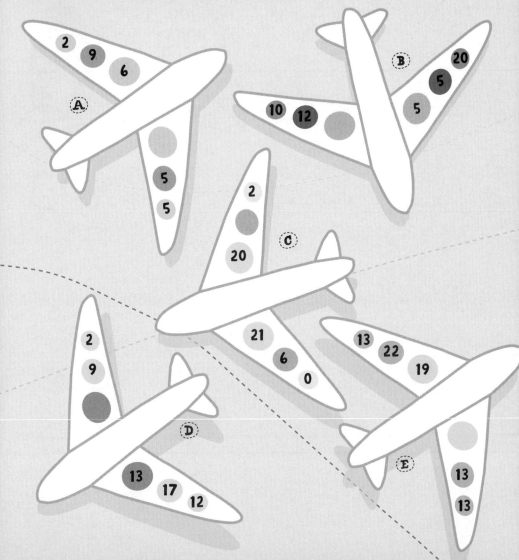

Fill in the missing numbers so that each plane has the same total on both wings. The plane with the largest total will take off first. Which will it be?

Draw a rocket

Follow the steps below to draw a space rocket.

① **Draw an outline.** ② **Add fins and boosters.** ③ **Add a window, door and details.** ④ **Shade it in and blast off!**

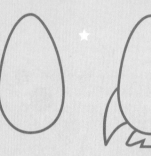

Four fences

Draw four straight fences to separate the cows.

Patchwork puzzle

Draw around the two blocks of squares in the patchwork
pattern that match the pieces shown below.

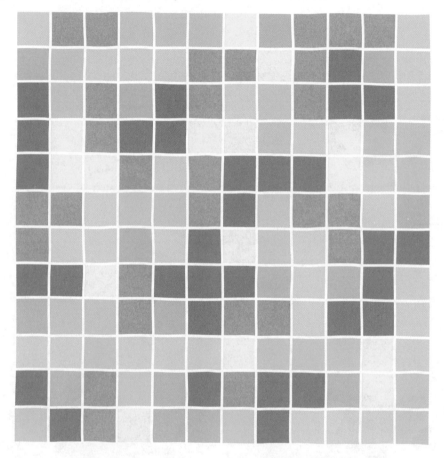

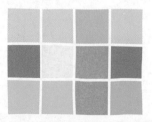

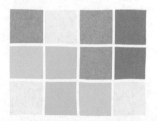

Spot the difference

Spot seven differences in the second scene.

Cupcake machine

Number the tops of the pipes to show where each topping comes from, in the order they are added to the cakes.

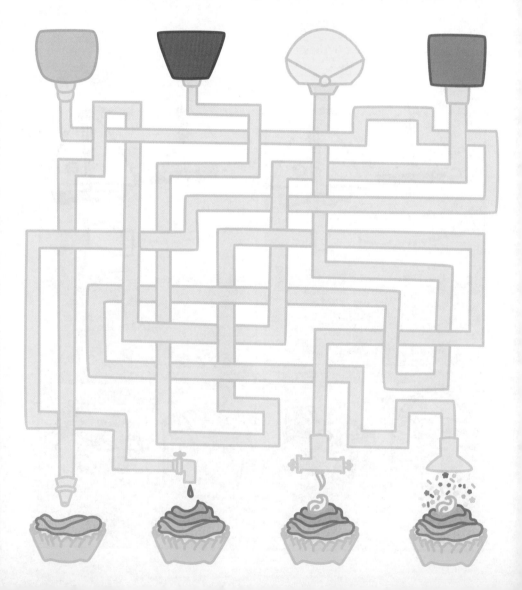

Balloon cities

Each hot-air balloon has half a famous city name on it.
Complete the city names by linking the correct balloons.

Just a maze

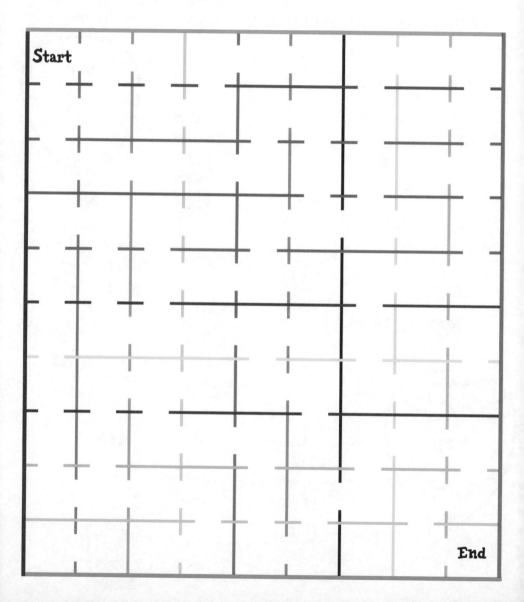

Find your way through the maze.

Start

End

183

Fact or fantasy?

① Bulgarians shake their heads for 'yes' and nod for 'no.'

② South Africans yawn when they're excited.

③ The first fortune cookies came from China.

④ Women in Nepal wear their wedding rings through their noses.

⑤ Gustave Eiffel, the French designer of the Eiffel Tower, also designed New York's Statue of Liberty.

⑥ In Brazil, people pull your ears on your birthday.

⑦ The Irish are the tallest people.

⑧ Sydney is the capital of Australia.

⑨ The Spanish national anthem has no words.

⑩ One in five Africans live in Nigeria.

Risky railway

Help this train to reach the station, avoiding all the lines
blocked by obstacles.

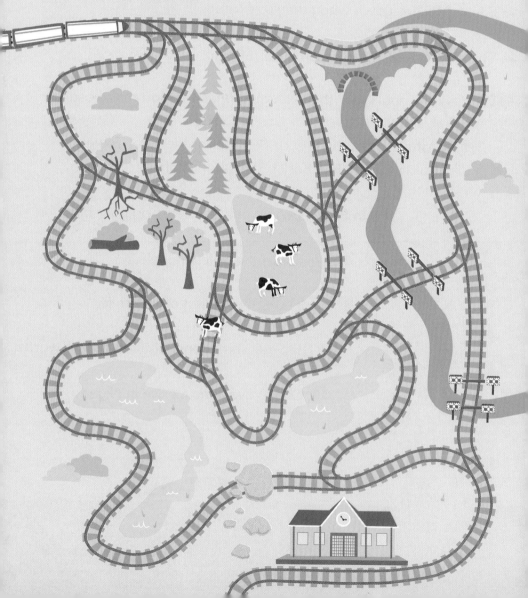

Souvenir mugs

This shop sells souvenir city mugs – but one of them is out of place. Find it and circle it.

I ♥ Paris

I ♥ Madrid

I ♥ London

I ♥ New York

I ♥ Vienna

I ♥ Rome

I ♥ Cats

I ♥ Prague

I ♥ Florence

I ♥ Chicago

I ♥ Miami

I ♥ Venice

Instructions

for Fortune teller (41), Dare snapper (97),
Snapping eagle (129) and Snapping gecko (175)

(1)

Crease along both
dotted lines

(2)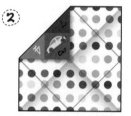

Fold corners in along
these lines

(3)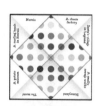

Turn paper over

(4)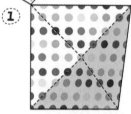

Fold corners in

(5)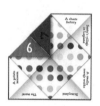

Crease square in half,
in both directions

(6)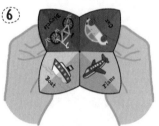

Open out
fortune teller

**To play with Fortune
teller and Dare
snapper:**

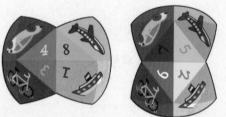

wide mouth   long mouth

1 Ask your friend to pick one of the words. (For example, 'Boat'.)
2 Spell it out on the fortune teller. ('B' open long mouth, 'O' open wide mouth...)
3 Stop on the last letter and ask your friend to pick one of the numbers.
4 Count it out on the fortune teller. ('1' open wide mouth, '2' open long mouth...)
5 Stop on the last number and ask your friend to pick one of the numbers.
6 Open its flap to reveal your friend's message.

Instructions

188

for Chatty penguin (32) and Croaking frog (118)

1

Fold in half
(picture on
the outside)

2

Cut or tear
along dotted
line (mouth)

3

Crease both
flaps back
and behind

4

Open and fold
in half (picture
on the inside)

5

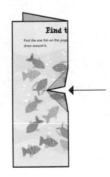

Push flaps
through

6

Squeeze page
to open mouth

Instructions

for Staring owl (64), Monster (76) and Curious cat (141)

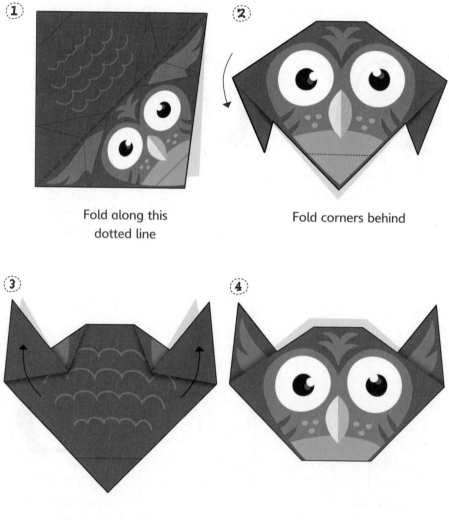

1. Fold along this dotted line

2. Fold corners behind

3. Turn over and fold corner tips up

4. Fold bottom corners in to stand model upright

Instructions

for Clown face (15), Space rocket (51) and Tiger face (157)

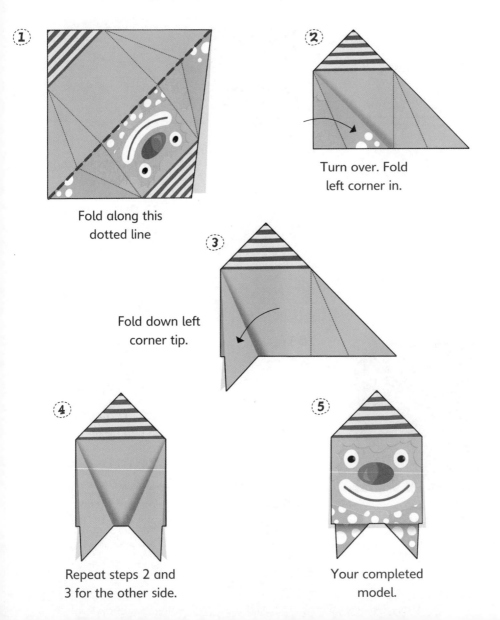

1 Fold along this dotted line

2 Turn over. Fold left corner in.

3 Fold down left corner tip.

4 Repeat steps 2 and 3 for the other side.

5 Your completed model.

Answers

1 Tunnel traffic
Fastest: 5
Slowest: 4

2 Crazy carousel

4 Travel times
Car journey

6 Triangle tiles

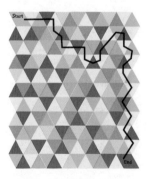

7 Countries quiz
1.c 2.b 3.a
4. bullfights 5.b
(It's called Machu
Picchu.) 6.a 7.c

8 Flag challenge

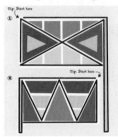

This is one way to do it

9 Treasure hunt

10 Bug box

11 Canoe camp

12 Flying home

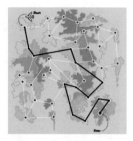

13 Excess baggage
The 18kg bag

18 Campers beware...
Bears

21 Seashore search

22 Airport race
White plane

24 Treasure maze

Answers

25 Magic square

2	7	6
9	5	1
4	3	8

27 Optical illusion
Separate circles
Illusion ©Prof. Baingio Pinna

28 Across the sea

30 Adding apples

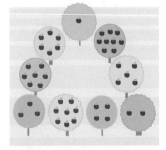

31 Find the fish

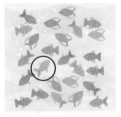

33 Explorers quiz
1.c 2.c 3.c 4.b 5.a
6. Bottom of the ocean
7. Christopher Columbus

34 Tower maze

36 Air traffic
17

37 Spy climb

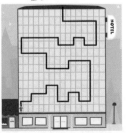

39 Sail the seas quiz
1.c 2. Submarine
3. Longships 4.b
5. Hammocks 6.b 7.a

42 Pier puzzle

43 Sorting stems

45 Hidden picture

46 Bees or spiders?
Eight bees, four spiders

Answers

47 Fairground maze

48 Word cross
1.p 2.n 3.g 4.e

49 Spaghetti junction
Blue car

50 Divide the world

54 Packing penguins
Line 3

57 Fact or fiction?
1. Fiction 2. Fiction
3. Fact 4. Fiction
5. Fact 6. Fact
7. Fiction 8. Fiction
9. Fiction 10. Fact (in 1961)

58 Crossword

59 Dot-to-dot

60 Code breaker
Agent X: MEET ME AT THE RAILWAY STATION AT HALF PAST SEVEN I WILL WEAR A RED BOW TIE X
Agent Z: WARNING ENEMY SPIES AT THE STATION MEET ME AT THE LIBRARY AT FIVE Z

61 A dangerous journey

63 Seashore jumble
11

65 The dragon's hoard

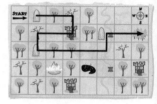

66 Optical illusion
False: they're parallel

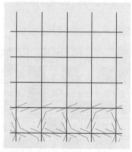

67 Animal quiz
1. The Abominable Snowman
2. Polar bears
3. b
4. a
5. True
6. Fat
7. Blood
8. b

68 Star-crossed
Hollywood

Answers

70 Find the bag

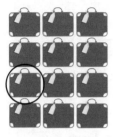

73 Desert maze

74 Riddle grid
Stamp

75 Optical illusion
Most people see
them disappear

77 Giraffe's supper
Four hours

78 Food cube B

79 Truth or lie
1. Lie 2. Truth 3. Truth
4. Lie 5. Lie (70% is
covered by water)
6. Truth 7. Lie 8. Lie

82 Baggage stack

83 Mountain lodge

85 Jungle grid
g6 b4 b3 e3

89 Weather symbols
Sun = 5   Snowflake = 1
Rainbow = 3   Cloud = 4
Missing = Snowflake

90 Flying saucers

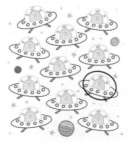

92 Optical illusion
Yes, for most people.

93 Travel quiz
1. Northeast 2. a
3. c 4. b 5. c
6. Madame Tussauds
7. Atlantic Ocean

95 Capital cities

China – Beijing
Guyana – Georgetown
Germany – Berlin
Kenya – Nairobi
Canada – Ottawa
Australia – Canberra

99 Spot the spots 28

101 Airport Gate 4

102 Animal
true or false
1. False 2. False
3. True 4. True
5. False 6. False
7. True 8. True
9. True 10. False

Answers

103 Optical illusion
False

105 Clever flowers

106 Time zones
Red clock: Mumbai
Green clock: Istanbul
Blue clock: Paris
Yellow clock: London
Purple clock: Moscow

107 Dot-to-dot

110 Riddles
1. Fire
2. A shirt
3. A hole
4. A candle
5. A sponge
6. An egg
7. A tennis ball
8. Breath

114 Dominoes

116 Perching parrots

117 Busy bee maze

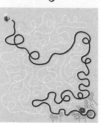

120 Go-fast fuel

121 Flags quiz

2. Jamaica   1. France

4. Germany   3. Japan

124 Up in the air quiz
1. London to New York
2. c 3. False 4. c 5. b

126 Lots of Labels
Four more

127 Cluttered campsite

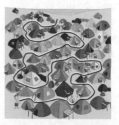

Answers

130 Tasty search

132 Waterhole maze

134 Link words

1. Paper
2. Bag
3. Man
4. Fish
5. Suit
6. Nut
7. Pan

135 O or X?

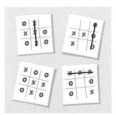

137 Dot-to-dot

138 Boomerang mix-up

140 Mini-sudoku

4	1	2	3
3	2	1	4
1	4	3	2
2	3	4	1

142 Ski run

143 Landmarks quiz

1. a 2. c 3. Asia
4. a 5. b 6. a 7. c

146 Even and odd

147 Get packing

149 One-way maze

150 Where in the world?
Rio de Janeiro

Answers

151 True or false?
1.F 2.T 3.T 4.F 5.T
6.F 7.T 8.F 9.F 10.T

152 Optical illusion
It disappears

155 Balloon flight

156 Famous characters
1. Robin Hood
2. Matilda
3. Ebenezer Scrooge
4. Alice 5. Mario
6. James Bond
7. Cinderella

159 Diver in danger!

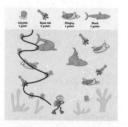

160 Picture sudoku

164 Pyramid maze

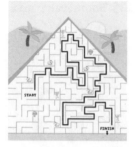

165 Sunshine Isle
1.c 2.d 3.a
4.e 5.b

166 Packing for Paradise
Barbados

167 Butterfly hunt
Lily: 21
Maddie: 17
Benji: 9

171 Balloon pattern

172 Fairground game

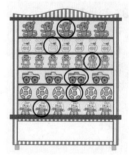

176 Busy airport
A. 7
B. 8
C. 5
D. 31
E. 28
Plane E takes off first